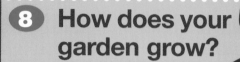

Hello!

And a big welcome to the second *Girl Talk Annual*. You'll find stacks of new stuff inside to keep you busy all year round – along with a few of your old favourites, of course! So no matter what time of year it is when you pick this up, have fun and get busy! Merry Christmas, Happy Easter and have a fantastic summer holiday!
Love,

Claire

The editor

Girl Talk's *Cover girl*

Name:
Marie Duffy
Age: ten
Hobbies: dancing, singing and playing football
Favourite star:
Michael Owen
Ambition: to be a children's TV presenter

inside...

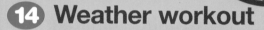
❀ Cover photo: Jamie Hughes
❀ Top: Girlheaven ❀ Teddy: Queens
❀ Hair accessories: Tinkerbell and Select
❀ Hairstylist: Karen Fundell

EDITOR CLAIRE FUNGE ART EDITOR CAROL GOOK PRODUCTION EDITOR ROBBIE KELLY

WRITE TO:
Girl Talk, Room A1130, Woodlands, 80 Wood Lane, London, W12 0TT

girltalk.magazine@bbc.co.uk

FRIENDS FOREVER!

Are you a good friend? Play the game on page 34 and see!

INSTRUCTIONS

To prepare your counters, carefully cut round the dotted lines and stick them on to stiff cardboard. Do the same thing with the spinner and then put a toothpick through the centre to spin it with. Now you're ready to play!

The rules

This fun board game can be played by two to five people. The object of the game is to be the first to reach the finish. Spin to see who goes first. The person with the highest number starts. Then spin to move your counter. Follow the instructions along the way. The winner is the player who makes it to the finish first.

The all-new adventures of Sweet Va...

RUNAWAY HAMSTER
Part 1

Pictures: David Watts
Script: Carol Warwick

Will Jessica change her mind about Tinkerbell? Read part 2 on page 6

5

Yuck! Here are your horrible seeds.

Jessica, come here!

I'm busy. What do you want, Steven?

Come and see what I've built.

Oh, all right. It had better be good.

It's a mousetrap I've made for science class.

She won't! Come on, we've got to find her. Help me look.

She must be in the house somewhere.

Poor Tinkerbell. I wonder if she's scared.

We're going to be in big trouble with Mum, and at school.

Don't all hamsters look alike?

So we'll buy a hamster that is Tinkerbell's twin. Isn't that a good idea?

I guess so.

It will! Nobody can tell *us* apart.

Will anyone notice the difference? The story continues on page 56

Pictures: David Watts
Script: Carol Warwick

We've got some cool ideas for keeping your green fingers busy all year round – whether you have a garden or not!

SPRING

SOMETHING FRUITY

YOU WILL NEED
- Pineapple top
- Large plant pot
- Pebbles or stones
- Clear plastic bag and tie
- Compost

For an impressive spiky house plant cut the top off a pineapple, leaving about 2cm of the fruit attached. Turn it on its side to dry for 48 hours. Place a layer of pebbles in a plant pot for drainage, then fill with potting compost almost to the top. Plant the pineapple covering the fruit base with compost. Water well then put the whole pot into a clear plastic bag and tie this at the top above the leaves. This acts as a mini greenhouse and helps the plant to grow roots. Keep it on a warm windowsill. Untie the bag after a couple of weeks and remove it completely once the plant starts to grow new leaves.

HOUSE PLANTS FOR FREE

YOU WILL NEED
- Spider or piggyback plants
- Compost
- Small plant pots

Spider plants (*Chlorophytum*) and piggyback plants (*Tolmiea*) will both grow to make exciting trailing plants for your bedroom. Their long, stems will also produce loads of new, free, plants. New plantlets from a piggyback plant sprout from the base of a mature leaf while the spider plant grows baby plants on long trailing stems. In both cases you simply cut off a plantlet and plant it in a pot of compost. Make sure you keep the mature leaf attached to the piggyback plantlet. Place your new plants in a warm bright spot and always keep the soil moist. Feed with a liquid feed during spring and summer. If you end up with a surplus of plants, you can always give them away to your friends.

SUMMER

FLOWER POWER

YOU WILL NEED
- Flowers
- Sheets of paper
- Sheets of card
- Heavy books

The garden is bursting with beautiful blooms during the summer months. There are so many around that it's a good idea to preserve a few by pressing them. Although you can buy flower presses, it's quite simple to put together a home-made one. Arrange your flowers between two sheets of paper, making sure they don't overlap, then sandwich this between two sheets of card. Put this on a flat surface in a warm dry spot and place a couple of heavy books on top. After two weeks the flowers will be dry and can be used to decorate cards or make pictures.

REACH FOR THE SKY

YOU WILL NEED
- Sunflower seeds
- Flower pots
- Compost
- Bamboo canes
- String

It wouldn't be summer without a few cheery sunflower heads peering out from the garden borders. Seed should be sown from March to May in small flower pots. Plant the seed 1.5cm deep and water well. Keep the soil moist and when the plant has grown and there are no more night-time frosts outside, you can transfer them to a sunny spot in the garden. You will need to support your sunflowers as they grow. Push

a bamboo cane into the ground and loosely tie the plant to it with string. Sunflowers can grow up to 3m tall. Why not have a competition with your friends to see who can grow the tallest?

THE ITALIAN JOB
YOU WILL NEED
✿ Spaghetti marrow seeds

There is a fascinating type of marrow that is known as the spaghetti marrow because when it is cooked its flesh looks like long, thin strands of pasta. To grow your own, just plant seeds in the ground in late May or early June. Keep them well watered and fed. First they will produce bright yellow flowers followed by the marrows.
To cook your marrow place it in a pan of boiling water and simmer for about 25 minutes until it is soft. Cut it in half

to reveal the spaghetti-like flesh. It is delicious served with garlic butter or with a home-made tomato sauce.

AUTUMN

A POT OF BULBS
YOU WILL NEED
✿ Glass vase
✿ Narcissus "Paper White" bulbs
✿ Gravel or pebbles

Autumn is the time of year for planting bulbs, but they are not just for the garden. For a cool indoor display, plant some Narcissus "Paper White" bulbs – a type of daffodil – in a vase of gravel or pebbles. Fill a glass vase three-quarters full with gravel or pebbles. Place your bulbs on top of this with the pointy bit to the top. Pour water into the vase so that it just reaches the bottom of the bulbs then top the vase up with the gravel or pebbles to hold the bulbs in place, but *not* cover them. Keep the water topped up and a display of delicate white daffodil blooms should appear within six to eight weeks.

WINTER

SPIT IT OUT AND POT IT UP
YOU WILL NEED
✿ Orange pips
✿ Crocks or stones
✿ Compost
✿ Plant pot
✿ Plastic bag and elastic band

As Christmas approaches, the shops will have loads of citrus fruit for sale. They are absolutely delicious, but don't just discard the pips – use them to grow a beautiful indoor plant. Place bits of broken pot (crocks) or stones in the bottom of a flower pot for drainage. Fill the pot with compost

then plant the pip about 1cm deep. Cover it up with a plastic bag to add humidity and help the pip to grow. Keep it on a warm sunny windowsill and remove the plastic bag when three to four leaves have developed.

CITRUS DELIGHT
YOU WILL NEED
✿ Oranges, lemons, limes

Citrus fruit can also be used for decoration. Take a selection of oranges, limes and lemons and slice them very thinly across the segments with a sharp knife to give you a cross section of the fruit. Put the slices on a nonstick backing sheet, making sure they don't overlap. Then place this on the bottom shelf of an oven at its lowest temperature setting or in a warm airing cupboard until the slices are completely dry and don't feel sticky to touch. The dried fruit can be hung up as Christmas tree decorations, added to a seasonal potpourri or used to decorate cards and pictures.

Always ask an adult to help if you need to use the oven or sharp knives.

✿ Words: Julie Hawker ✿ *Tolmiea* (piggyback plant) pictures: Stephen Marwood for *Gardeners' World* ✿ *Helianthus* (sunflower) seeds picture: *Gardeners' World* ✿ *Helianthus* "Orit" (sunflower) picture: Ian McKinnel for *Gardeners' World* ✿ Pineapple pictures: Peter Dürkes for *Gardeners' World* ✿ Daffodil bulb pictures: Julian Hawkins for *Gardeners' World*

Maria was mad about ponies. She loved riding them and grooming them. She didn't even mind mucking out. "You spend too much time with those ponies," said Dan, her younger brother. "You've got pony fever if you ask me." Maria shrugged. "Well, I didn't ask you, did I? And if there was anything wrong with me," she said, "I would talk to a doctor, not a donkey. Thank you very much."

"Huh!" said Dan. "You think you're going to win the show jumping at the gymkhana, don't you? Well, you're not. India Nosworthy will win that. She has the best pony around here and she always wins. So there."

"It's the taking part that's important – not the winning," said Maria, pulling on her riding boots.

As Maria left her brother scowling over his stamp collection, she knew that he had been right. India Nosworthy was a year younger than Maria, but she had won the competition every year that Maria could remember – even beating her elder sister, Anne-Marie. It wasn't that India was such a great horsewoman, but Somerset Downs III was such a beautiful jumper. He was quite an old pony, but very clever. He was a bay, with a mane and tail to match. Maria loved to watch him sail over the fences, his reddish-brown tail swishing all the while.

❖ Illustrations: Carol Daniel

Winter sun

It was cold and still dark, and Maria was feeling cross and grumpy. But as she reached the stables her mood brightened considerably. How lovely it was there. Her pony, Jumble, was pleased to see her. Jumble had such a loveable personality, but he was a dull, grey and untidy-looking pony. He threw his head

R JUMBLE

a story by
Davey Moore

card," said Maria, and Jumble's little grey ears pricked up. As Maria turned down Hawthorn Lane she saw another two riders ahead. "Oh no!" thought Maria. "It's India Nosworthy and her sister Anne-Marie."

Anne-Marie was riding Cajun, a glossy black six-year-old with a thick, proud-looking mane. India was on Somerset Downs, of course. Somerset Downs, a beautiful chestnut, had a blaze on his forehead that looked for all the world to Maria like a genie escaping from a bottle. Anne-Marie waved at Maria to join them. Maria had never spoken to Anne-Marie before. She seemed nice. But India ignored her as usual. They all trotted together for a while. Anne-Marie chatted to Maria about the event. "I was hoping to compete, but it's my birthday the day before and that one day will make me a year too old. It's so silly, isn't it?"

"It is a bit," Maria nodded.

"I'm winning!"

"Hey, you two," India suddenly piped up. "How about a race to that stream over there?" Maria wasn't sure. She knew India was bound to win and thought that it was probably just a trick to show up poor old Jumble. "Well," said Maria, "I don't know…"

back in real pleasure at seeing Maria. "Hello, Jumble," she said. "You always brighten up these yucky dark mornings for me!" After she had mucked out, Maria tacked up and set off down the road from the yard. The countryside was luminous with the first milky light of the day. Drops of dew had frozen like glass beads on the bare tree branches. "It's like a Christmas

continues over

"Oh, come on!" said India "It will be good exercise for the ponies, and we can jump the low hedge between here and the stream."

"Let's do it, Maria," said Anne-Marie. "It will be great practice for the gymkhana."

"Okay, guys," said Maria and before she knew it the two sisters were galloping away. Jumble leapt as he started to chase after the others. He seemed eager to join in the fun. Anne-Marie and Cajun took the lead, but it wasn't long before India caught up.

"I'm winning!" India cried as Somerset nudged out in front.

"Come on, Jumble," said Maria. "Let's show them what you can do."

Jumble seemed inspired. He ate up the distance, drawing closer and closer to the two leading ponies.

Now Maria and Jumble were galloping alongside Anne-Marie, who cried out, "Whoo-ooo! Isn't this fun?" Maria was too exhilarated to reply.

"India – will have to – slow down – to jump the hedge," gasped Anne-Marie. "She sometimes misjudges – Somerset's stride – at speed."

Sure enough, at the hedge India had a real problem. The big chestnut pony raised his chocolate-coloured tail and shied at the obstacle.

"Oh, come on, Somerset!" said India. "Do behave." She pulled his heavy head back towards the hedge. This was disastrous for Jumble. As he approached the jump, Somerset Downs swerved in front of the grey pony. Startled, Jumble reared up and unseated his rider before tumbling into the hedge himself. Maria saw the ground coming up towards her. She threw out her hands and rolled over and over in the long, wet grass.

Gone lame

"Oof!" she gasped, jarring to a halt. She was lying on her back staring at the pale sky.

She felt as if her bones had been shaken up like dice in a cup. Seconds later Anne-Marie's concerned face appeared in the sky above her. "Are you all right, Maria?" she asked.

Maria did a little test, moving her arms and legs carefully. Everything hurt, but everything seemed to be

working okay. But what about Jumble? Maria jumped up and, wobbling, almost fell straight back down. Anne-Marie took her arm and supported her.

"Oooh. Ow!" said Maria.

"Never mind me, what about Jumble?"

"I was winning until then," said India, who hadn't even bothered to dismount.

"Pity we'll have to stop. Your funny old pony has gone lame by the look of him."

Sure enough, poor Jumble was not his usual happy self. Maria walked him back to the stable and the vet was called to examine him.

Mr Masters ran his hands skilfully over the injured fetlock then said that it was just a rather nasty sprain.

"However, I'm afraid Jumble will have to miss the gymkhana," he said. "We must give him time to recover."

The following morning Maria was alone with Jumble. She felt sad as she sat in the straw, chatting in a soothing voice to her pony. But she knew it was Jumble she should really feel sorry for, not herself.

"Blast that India," said Maria. "She'll only go and win it again anyway."

"What did you say?" came a voice. Maria was startled. The voice was familiar, but she didn't recognise it straight away. She twisted round and squinted into the clear morning light coming through the top of the stable door. It was a girl.

Too ill

Maria held her hands up to her face and her eyes adjusted to the bright light. "Oh, er, hello, Anne-Marie," said Maria, blushing furiously. "I was just, er, saying, er, what a pity it is that I won't be able to compete in the competition."

"Maybe you can," said Anne-Marie, walking into the stable and closing the door behind her.

"I don't think so," said Maria. "Not with Jumble out of action."

"Who said anything about riding Jumble?" said Anne-Marie. "India woke up this morning aching all over with flu. She tried to pretend she was all right, but Mum would have none of it and sent her straight back to bed. She's going to be wrapped up nice and warm for the rest of the week. She'll be well enough to watch, but too ill to compete. That's definite."

"So she's not going to take part in the gymkhana?" said Maria.

"No," said Anne-Marie, sitting down on the straw next to Maria. "And neither will Somerset Downs – unless you want to ride him."

Maria's mouth made the shape of an O. Then that was the sound that came out of it, too. "Oh!" she said. "Oh, I couldn't."

"Why ever not?" asked Anne-Marie. "I certainly can't," she went on. "I'm too old, after all. And poor Jumble here can't jump. I admired the way you rode yesterday afternoon up until the accident – and the way you're caring for Jumble now. Somerset is a beautiful pony. It would be a shame for you both to miss the competition."

"Well, when you put it like that," Maria smiled, "how could I refuse?"

Trial ride

It seemed impossible that India and Anne-Marie could really be sisters. How could one be so nice and the other be so mean? But then Maria had a thought.

"What about India?" she said.

"What about her?" replied Anne-Marie.

"Won't she be really cross with me?" asked Maria.

"Only if you win," laughed Anne-Marie. "India knows that everyone thinks she wins every year because she has the best pony, although she insists it's because she's the best rider. It will be interesting to see how you get on with Somerset, Maria. Be here, ready, at seven o'clock sharp tomorrow morning. I have to take Cajun out for his exercise. You can come with me and have a trial ride on Somerset."

Maria hadn't made up her mind, but her heart took over and she said, "Tomorrow at seven, then. Sharp. I'll see you here."

"See you," said Anne-Marie, standing up and brushing the straw from her jodhpurs. Then she was gone, out into the morning sun. "Poor Jumble," said Maria, brushing away a lock of his untidy grey mane. "I *will* ride Somerset, but I'll do it for you!"

The next morning Maria and Anne-Marie rode together. Anne-Marie galloped ahead on Cajun. Somerset was very bouncy under Maria – to her he felt ten times more powerful than Jumble. She was a bit scared at first, but very quickly found herself getting used to him.

The jump-off

At the end of the first round there were only two riders with no penalty points against them – Natalie Serembezis on Godspeed and Maria Buckley on Somerset Downs III. The loudspeaker announced, "Ladies and gentlemen, the competition will now move into the next round – the jump-off. Fence two – the wall – and fence eight – the hedge and parallel poles – will both be raised."

It was a difficult test. Maria was nervous. She had to keep wiping her palms on her jodhpurs. Her tummy felt twisted and tight. She looked across at Natalie, the girl she was up against. Her pony, Godspeed, was jet black, just like Cajun. He rippled and shone like an oily puddle reflecting a thunderous sky. Natalie went first. Godspeed sailed over the fences and Natalie completed the round without a penalty point in one minute and 45 seconds. Maria would have to complete the round in an even better time. Somerset was excited and jumped off at a great gallop. Maria had to hold him back after the first fence. "Steady, Somerset," she said. "Steady." Together they did the next six jumps at a steady pace. There was only the eighth and the final dash to make up the time. But at the last hedge Somerset was

perplexed – as if reminded of the accident with Jumble at the hedge by the stream. "Come on, Somerset!" whispered Maria into his pointy chestnut-coloured ears. "Do it for Jumble!" It was as if the old bay understood. He leapt over the final fence as lightly as if he were that genie on his forehead. Together, Maria and Somerset Downs III won with seconds to spare!

"One minute and 42 seconds," the time was announced over the loudspeaker.

Everyone cheered for Somerset, and for Maria. Maria knew her mum and dad were watching – even her younger brother Dan was there. They would all be proud of her.

A first!

Anne-Marie had been watching the gymkhana. As had India, wrapped up in hand-knitted scarves and looking a bit like a home-made mummy.

"Well done, Maria," said Anne-Marie. "You put on a great show." With that, Anne-Marie gave India a nudge.

"Well done, Maria," said India. "I'm sorry about Jumble. Maybe when he's better we can go riding together."

"Yes," said Maria, smiling. "That would be nice. No races though! Oh, and thank you for letting me ride Somerset, India. It was really thrilling." India smiled at her. Now that *was* a first! Anne-Marie gave Maria a wink as India shuffled off, sniffling. Maria was so proud when she came back to the stables. She showed Jumble the rosette. Jumble was pleased to see her and the rosette, but especially pleased by the year's supply of nuts that came with it! ✿

PUZZLES

ON CLOUD 9

These four famous faces are feeling very happy with themselves. Can you work out who feels like they're floating on cloud nine?

WEATHERBEATEN!

The items in the word wheel are all useful in bad weather, and all have one missing letter in common. Unscramble the words and work out the missing letter

SO VANE!

Only two of these weather vanes are identical. Can you work out which ones?

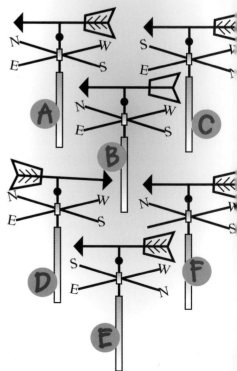

STORM IN A TEACUP
Find the answers and a make a din!

1 **This Roald Dahl heroine had very special powers**

2 **Conkers grow on horse _ _ _ _ _ _ _ _ trees**

3 **Mickey and Minnie _ _ _ _ _**

4 **There are 60 seconds in one of these**

5 **She had two ugly sisters**

6 **Where you will see Jamie, Beppe and Robbie**

7 **The Queen wears one of these on her head**

Boiling point

Camilla, Keely and Levi each have a different way of cooling down in the hot sunshine. Follow the lines to find out who does what

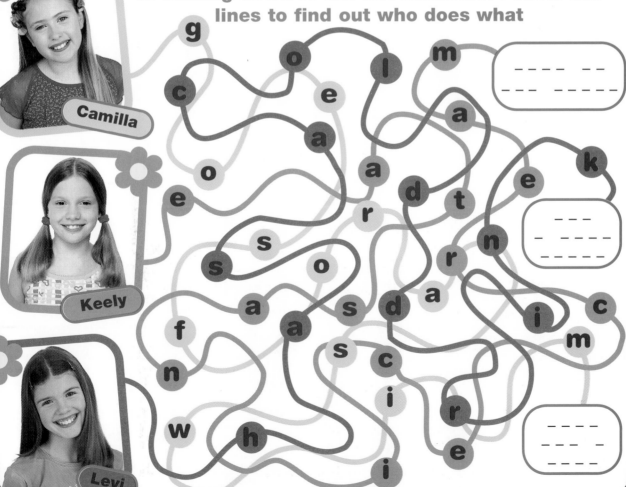

Camilla

Keely

Levi

Season's eatings!

Cook up a tasty treat at any time of year with all these great recipes from **Girl Talk**'s Vicky Musselman

SPRING

Rhubarb and custard trifle

Make the most of those fab early fruits that arrive with the spring. And what could be a scrummier way to use them than a trifle? Here's a really cool twist on boring old rhubarb and custard!

WHAT YOU NEED
- **450g fresh rhubarb**
- **50g light brown sugar**
- **½ a Madeira cake, cut into 6 pieces**
- **6 tbsp orange juice**
- **500g carton ready-made custard**
- **squirty cream and hundreds and thousands, to serve**

WHAT TO DO
1 **Wash and trim the rhubarb, discarding any leaves. Cut each stick into 2cm pieces. Put in a pan with the sugar. Heat gently until the sugar dissolves.**
2 **Cook over a medium heat for 5 minutes, stirring occasionally until the rhubarb is softened and cooked through. Allow to cool completely.**
3 **Put the Madeira cake into a large serving bowl and drizzle over it with the orange juice.**
4 **Spoon the rhubarb over the top of the cake. Pour over the custard, covering the rhubarb and smooth the top.**
5 **Squirt a layer of the cream on top of the custard then sprinkle this with hundreds and thousands. Serves four.**

SUMMER

Mini lamb burgers

The summer's really cookin' once the barbie comes out. And you can't find better finger food than a burger in a bun. No mess and no plate needed!

WHAT YOU NEED
- **500g lamb mince**
- **1 small onion, finely chopped**
- **1 tbsp tomato puree**
- **1 tsp dried mixed herbs**
- **lettuce leaves, sliced cucumber and 2 tomatoes, to serve**
- **8 small bread rolls, to serve**
- **tomato ketchup, to serve**

WHAT TO DO
1 **Put the lamb mince into a bowl with the onion, tomato purée and dried herbs.**
2 **Mix well with your hands until everything is evenly combined.**
3 **Now wet your hands, divide the mixture into eight and shape each one into a burger. (You may have to keep wetting your hands to prevent the mixture from sticking to you.)**
4 **Preheat the grill. Put the burgers on to a grill pan. Transfer to the grill and cook for 5–6 minutes on each side until the burgers are completely cooked through.**
5 **Meanwhile, make the salad. Wash the lettuce, cucumber and tomatoes. Slice the tomatoes. Put a burger into each bread roll and stuff with salad. Serve with a big dollop of tomato ketchup. Serves four.**

AUTUMN

Apple pancakes with caramel sauce

Autumn may be back-to-school season, but it's also the time for the best apples of the year. Here's a pan-tastic way to eat them!

WHAT YOU NEED
- **4 eating apples**
- **50g butter**
- **50g light brown sugar**
- **8 ready-made crêpe pancakes**
- **vanilla ice cream, to serve**
- **ready-made caramel sauce, to serve**

WHAT TO DO
1 **Peel and core the apples, then cut each one into 8 wedges.**
2 **Heat the butter in a large frying pan. When the butter foams add the apples and sprinkle over the sugar. Cook on a medium heat for 5 minutes, stirring occasionally until the apples are soft and tinged brown. Remove from the heat.**
3 **Spoon apple mixture into each pancake and fold into four, to make a triangle shape.**
4 **Put two pancakes on to each serving plate and top with a spoonful of vanilla ice cream.**
5 **Spoon over some of the caramel sauce and serve straight away.**
Quick tip
The caramel sauce is usually with the ice cream in supermarkets and ready-made pancakes can be found in the supermarket bread section.

Recipes: Vicky Musselman Illustrations: Rachel Fuller

WINTER

Cheesy eggy bread

Tuck into a plateful of this scrummy dish on a winter's day and feel your energy levels rise.

WHAT YOU NEED
- 2 eggs
- 4 tbsp milk
- 25g cheddar cheese, grated
- large knob of butter
- splash of oil
- 2 thick slices white bread
- 4 slices wafer-thin ham
- tomato ketchup, to serve

WHAT TO DO
1 Beat the eggs and milk in a shallow bowl with a fork. Sprinkle in the cheese and beat well. Season with pepper.
2 Heat the butter and oil in a large frying pan.
3 Dip both sides of the bread into the egg mixture. Add to the hot pan and cook for 2–3 minutes on each side until golden brown.
4 Serve with the ham and tomato ketchup. Serves two.

Real hot chocolate

On a chilly winter evening nothing beats a comforting cup of the most chocolatey hot choc around. In fact, the worse the weather outside, the more you'll enjoy it inside!

WHAT YOU NEED
- 2 mugfuls of milk
- 50g plain* chocolate, broken in small pieces
- 2 tsp light brown sugar
- 4–6 marshmallows
- 2 cinnamon sticks, to serve, optional

(*Please note, you must use plain chocolate for this recipe.)

WHAT TO DO
1 Pour the milk into a medium pan and heat over a medium heat.
2 When little bubbles appear around the edges add the chocolate, whisking all the time with a balloon whisk until the chocolate melts. (You may need to reduce the temperature to prevent the milk from getting too hot).
3 As soon as all the chocolate has melted, add the sugar and remove from the heat. Carefully pour into the mugs, then drop in 2 or 3 marshmallows. Drink warm. Serves two.

Ask an adult to help you with these recipes

WHICH TV SHOW WOULD YOU PRESENT?

Have you got what it takes to join the Blue Peter team, present Top of the Pops or be a Really Wild Show star? Find out with our telly-tastic quiz

1 **Your pals are coming round for the day. What do you get up to together?**
a) Write a play, make some scenery and put on a show for your parents.
b) Take your dog out for a walk then give him a wash and brush-up.
c) Ask your mates to bring round their CDs and make up dance routines to your favourite songs.

2 **What would you never leave the house without?**
a) A torch, sewing kit and compass – you never know when they might come in handy.
b) You take binoculars with you to help you spot wildlife, and a pad and pen to keep a record of what you see.
c) A personal stereo and as many tapes as you can carry.

Words: Jenny Simmons ✿ Illustrations: Katy Taggart

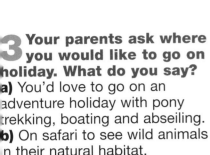

3 Your parents ask where you would like to go on holiday. What do you say?
a) You'd love to go on an adventure holiday with pony trekking, boating and abseiling.
b) On safari to see wild animals in their natural habitat.
c) You'll go anywhere, as long as you can take your radio.

4 What is your favourite subject at school?
a) PE is the best – all that fast-paced fun keeps you on your toes.
b) You prefer feeding the school hamster to doing any lessons.
c) Music is your fave subject – you can't wait to get your hands on the xylophone!

5 What do you have on your bedroom wall?
a) A calendar you made from old magazine pictures and sticky-back plastic.
b) Photos of your pets and pictures of fluffy animals.
c) Giant posters of all the top pop stars.

6 What would be your idea of a perfect day out?
a) Tackling an assault course in the morning, then off to a museum for the afternoon.
b) Going on a nature trail then helping out at the local animal shelter.
c) Buying a new sparkly outfit and wearing it to see your favourite band in concert.

7 One of your friends is having a fancy-dress party. What do you wear?
a) You find out what a girl your age would have worn 100 years ago, then make yourself an outfit.
b) Fluffy clothes and face paints transform you into a character from the musical *Cats*.
c) You and three pals dig out your denims and dress up as B*Witched.

8 Your best friend has a bad cold. How do you cheer her up?
a) Pick her some flowers from the garden and make her a get-well card.
b) Clean out her rabbit's hutch and bring him in for a cuddle.
c) Choose some cheery songs and put them all on a special tape for her to listen to.

★ HOW DID YOU SCORE? ★

Mostly A's
Grab your double-sided sticky tape and get ready because you're the perfect presenter for *Blue Peter*. You're just bursting with ideas for exciting expeditions, places to explore and things to make and do. You love trying new things and you never sit still. All of your friends agree – there's never a dull moment when you're around!

Mostly B's
Move over Michaela, *The Really Wild Show* is definitely the programme for you. When you're not feeding, grooming or playing with your pets, you're making a fuss of someone else's. To you, even mucky jobs are fun when there are animals involved. You belong to loads of wildlife clubs and you love watching vet programmes on TV. You really are animal crackers!

Mostly C's
You're so music mad, you've probably got the radio on while you're reading this. That's why you'd make a fantastic *Top of the Pops* presenter. You know exactly what's in the charts and can't wait to find out everything about your favourite bands. Your bedroom walls are covered in so many pop posters you can't remember what colour your wallpaper is.

It's in the stars

What does your star sign say about you? Find out with our sparkling guide to the zodiac

Aries
21 March–20 April

You're a real lively lass who loves to be the centre of attention. Bursting with confidence, you're not afraid to tackle anything, from acting in the school play to abseiling down a cliff. But if there's nothing to do, you're the first to complain about being bored. You can be a bit bossy, but your friends forgive you because you're such fun to be with.

Cosmic colour **red**
Celeb **Katy Hill**

Taurus
21 April–21 May

Tidy Taurus girls just can't help clearing up after everyone. You wouldn't dream of dropping your clothes on the bedroom floor or leaving the top off the toothpaste! You're fab at cooking and love making things like birthday cards and bookmarks. Once you've started something you always see it through to the end – and then tidy up afterwards!

Cosmic colour **navy blue**
Celeb **Jo from S Club 7**

Gemini
22 May–21 June

Geminis are the jokers of the zodiac. You have your pals in stitches with your quick-fire gags and cheeky impressions. You find it difficult to concentrate on anything for very long and you are always getting told off for chatting in class. In fact, talking on the phone is your favourite pastime and you always know all the gossip.

Cosmic colour **yellow**
Celeb **J from Five**

Cancer
22 June–23 July

If you spend your spare time feeding stray cats or helping your gran do her shopping, you're bound to be a caring Cancer. Although you can be a bit shy with people you don't know, you love spending time with your close friends. Your ideal evening would be a night in watching a really soppy animal movie with one of your best mates.

Cosmic colour **lilac**
Celeb **Konnie Huq**

❀ Words: Jenny Simmons

Leo

24 July–23 August

Wild Leos just love to party. You never miss an opportunity to put on your glittery gear and get dancing. When you're not bopping away, you spend your spare time performing at a drama club or playing sports. Leos enjoy all kinds of games and are top team players – as long as they can be the captain!

Cosmic colour **gold**
Celeb **Kate Sanderson**

Virgo

24 August–23 September

The neatest sign of the zodiac has got to be Virgo. You wear smart outfits, keep your bedroom neat and tidy and even store your CDs in alphabetical order! A Virgo girl likes everything to be perfect and you get really cross with yourself whenever you make a mistake in your homework or spill something down your clothes.

Cosmic colour **white**
Celeb **Tina from S Club 7**

Libra

24 September–23 October

Shop till you drop – that's your motto! Librans love clothes and always flick straight to the fashion pages of a magazine. You can spend hours choosing a hot new outfit or carefully converting your old gear to the latest look. But your favourite hobby is swapping clothes with your mates as it's the easiest way to get a whole new wardrobe!

Cosmic colour **pink**
Celeb **Nicky from Westlife**

Scorpio

24 October–22 November

Want to know a secret? Then don't bother asking a Scorpio girl! You mysterious minxes love getting other people to confide in you, but won't reveal anything about yourselves. Your diary is always locked and hidden away and anyone who dares to sneak a peek should watch out – Scorpios may seem quiet, but they have a sting in their tail.

Cosmic colour **orange**
Celeb **Lisa from Steps**

Sagittarius

23 November–21 December

If there's one day of the year that Sagittarians really look forward to, it's sports day! What better opportunity to get active and show off your sporty skills? And even when you're not competing, you still have a fab time cheering on your mates. You love going to new places and meeting new people and your ambition is to travel all over the world.

Cosmic colour **purple**
Celebs **Edele and Keavy from B*Witched**

Capricorn

22 December–20 January

If you want to plan an outing or arrange a party, ask a Capricorn – they are the most organised star sign! You Capricorns love planning ahead and wouldn't dream of doing anything without finding out all about it first. Your fave pastimes are reading, surfing the internet and doing school projects, and you're always top of the class!

Cosmic colour **green**
Celeb **Matt Baker**

Aquarius

21 January–19 February

It's easy to spot an Aquarian – you love to look different, so you always stand out in a crowd. You may have lots of friends, but you like to do things your own way and you don't care what other people think. Aquarians are very creative and you often make your own clothes and jewellery as it's the only way to get an outfit funky enough for your wild and wacky tastes.

Cosmic colour **light blue**
Celeb **Emma Bunton**

Pisces

20 February–20 March

Pisces girls go with the flow. You'd much rather spend time gazing out the window, than doing anything practical. Kind, helpful and polite, you hate it when people hurt your feelings so you're always nice to everyone. Pisceans are usually very calm, except when they hear about people being nasty to animals – then these friendly fishes turn into angry sharks!

Cosmic colour **silver**
Celeb **Kirsten O'Brien**

Reading

"How was the walk?" called out Bev Hawkins, walking through from the kitchen. "Great!" replied Tess from the hallway as she and her dad took off their walking boots and jackets. "We walked seven miles and Dad allowed me to read the map and compass!" "You know she's really getting the hang of it, Bev," said Ted Hawkins. "We didn't get lost once!"

Homework

"By the way, Tess," said Bev, "Maria called."
"Maria? What did she want, Mum?" asked Tess.
"She wondered if you could help her with her French homework – she's having some problems with it," said Bev, handing over Maria's number.
After dinner Tess went to her room. "This is just typical," she muttered. "Maria and her friends ignore me at school, but when it comes to helping out with homework, they never have any trouble asking me for answers. Well, not this time!" With that, she tore up Maria's number.
The next day at school, Tess's teacher handed out letters to all of her students.
"These letters are about an activity week that will be taking place in a fortnight's time," announced Miss Baker. Tess sighed as the rest of the class cheered. She was never one for joining in. "So please have your mum or dad sign the consent form and return them to me." On the way home Tess was thinking about the dreaded activity week and how she could get out of it when someone shouted out her name.

"I've been shown how to do this at least a dozen times and I still don't get it!"

"Are you deaf?" laughed Maria as she caught up with Tess. "I've been calling you for ages."
"Sorry," replied Tess quietly.
"Did you get my message last night?" continued Maria, trying to catch her breath.

Bookworm

"What message?" Tess lied. Maria looked a little disappointed. "Oh well, it doesn't matter. Forget it." Tess was just about to tell Maria that she *had* received her message, and that she could come round to Tess's house to work on their French homework together when the girls heard another shout. "Hey, Maria! Why are you talking to Bookworm?" it was Melanie Gibbs, one of the trendiest girls from school.
"Don't mind her," said Maria looking awkward. "I think it's cool that you read so much. See you later."
Tess was called Bookworm at school because at break time you could always find her in a corner, reading a book.
"This activity week's going to be a nightmare!" Tess moaned to herself on the way home. Two weeks passed and Tess found herself in one of the dorms of Mountain View Activity Centre, along with Maria, Melanie, Jessica and Taylor – the class in-crowd.
"This week would be just great, if we didn't have to share with Bookworm," Melanie sneered.
"Leave it out, Mel," said Maria. "We all have to work as a team this week."
Tess smiled to herself. Maybe Maria wasn't so bad after all.

Rendezvous

That week Tess found herself taking part in activities she had never dreamt of doing before – mountain climbing, canoeing, dinghy sailing and abseiling. After breakfast on the last day Todd, the centre's activity leader, handed out a compass and a map to each group. "We've been showing you how to use

The Signs

A story by Jenny Wackett

"Because she's the one who's reading the map," Maria replied.

"Look, I do this kind of stuff with my dad," explained Tess. "We walk for miles with a map and compass and I've never got us lost once – trust me."

The rest of the girls shrugged their shoulders and followed Tess. Half an hour later the group found themselves at the rendezvous point.

"Well done, girls!" Todd congratulated them. "You're the first back!"

"Thanks to Tess," said Maria, giving Tess a quick hug.

Tess went red with embarrassment. "No, no, it was a team effort!" she said, as the others in the group patted her and hugged her, too.

"I hope we can be friends, now," said Maria to Tess, "because I've always wanted to be your friend."

"I'd really like that," said Tess. "And I'm sure if I had used my map-reading skills and read the signs earlier, we could have been friends sooner!" ✿

this equipment all week," he said. "Now you can show us how much you've learnt by reaching the rendezvous point marked on your maps."

"I've been shown how to do this at least a dozen times and I still don't get it!" said Taylor.

"Don't worry," said Maria smiling at Tess. "I'm sure we can do it."

Tess took the map and compass from Maria and quickly set her co-ordinates. "We have to go this way," she said, and then marched off at a brisk pace.

After a while Tess and her group noticed some of the other girls walking in a different direction.

Trust me

"Shouldn't we follow the rest of them?" asked Jessica.

"Why? They're going the wrong way," said Tess.

"How do you know that?" asked Melanie worriedly.

PUZZLES

IN THE SOUP

Feast your eyes on these fab soup flavours and see how many you can find hidden in the letter square

```
F V E G E T A B L E A X
X R L L X C G Q M F P M
O G E B E E E E O C T F I
C X I N D N O L R Z J N
E Q T X C R T A E O O E
T I Q A H H N I T R K S
O W P S I E O A L N Y T
M N U N K L T N R J U R
A M Z C R O J P I S Y O
T X I R P K P J Z O A N
O H N P E A S B A D N E
C D B E E F B R O T H N
```

OXTAIL CHICKEN LENTIL PEA
FRENCH ONION POTATO TOMATO
CELERY BEEF BROTH VEGETABLE
MUSHROOM MINESTRONE

Trifle Towers

Only two of these five trifles are identical. Can you spot the matching pair?

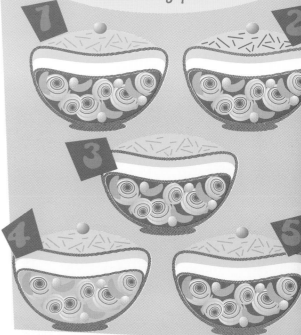

BISCUIT BARREL

Unscramble the names of the biscuits and spot the odd one out

OADRBTSHRE

NNITGEGRU

RDRCUAMESTAC

ROONBUB

WNDHECSAESEICH

TIPTOP TASTES

Each of the jumbled pizza toppings has a letter missing. Unscramble the words to reveal the pizza flavours and the one missing letter they all have in common

1. E O H T C A A T E D M T O N S

2. S E M U P R S U E P R

3. E I G A A N V R T

4. M A N H N I D I E P P A L

5. E P I P R O P N

6. M E A F A S T T

SWEET TOOTH

Using the clues on the right, make a new word by adding one letter to each word on the left. The missing letters spell an essential sweet ingredient

BET + ?= Better than the rest

PROD + ?= Having a high opinion of yourself

KIN + ?= Henry VIII was one of these

MEN + ?= Very stingy

COOK + ?= Thief

_ _ _ _ _ _ _ _ _

TASTY TEASER

Put the name of each object in the correct space to reveal a sweet treat in the shaded squares

JUST DESSERTS

One of these three fruits won't make it into the fruit salad. Can you work out which?

ANSWERS Tasty teaser Candle Stamp Bell Lemon Shoe Bone Cap Boat Pram The hidden word is chocolate. Sweet tooth Best Proud King Mean Crook The missing letters spell sugar. Biscuit barrel Ginger nut Custard cream Shortbread Cheese sandwich Bourbon Well, have you ever had a cheese-sandwich biscuit? Trifle towers Trifles 1 and 5 are identical Just desserts The apple doesn't make it into the fruit salad. Tiptop tastes Cheese and tomato Pepperoni Vegetarian Ham and pineapple Meat feast Super supreme The missing letter is E.

Girl TALK 2001 YEAR

NOTES

	JANUARY	FEBRUARY	MARCH	APRIL	MAY	JUNE
1	MON ✿ New Year's Day	THU	THU	SUN	TUE	FRI
2	TUE	FRI	FRI	MON	WED	SAT
3	WED	SAT	SAT	TUE	THU	SUN
4	THU	SUN	SUN	WED	FRI	MON
5	FRI	MON	MON	THU	SAT	TUE ✿ World Environment D
6	SAT	TUE	TUE	FRI	SUN	WED
7	SUN	WED	WED	SAT	MON ✿ May Bank Holiday	THU
8	MON	THU	THU	SUN	TUE	FRI
9	TUE	FRI	FRI ✿ Holi (Hindu spring festival)	MON	WED	SAT
10	WED	SAT	SAT	TUE	THU	SUN
11	THU	SUN	SUN	WED	FRI	MON
12	FRI	MON	MON ✿ Commonwealth Day	THU	SAT	TUE
13	SAT	TUE	TUE	FRI ✿ Good Friday	SUN	WED
14	SUN	WED ✿ Valentine's Day	WED	SAT	MON	THU
15	MON	THU	THU	SUN ✿ Easter Sunday	TUE	FRI
16	TUE	FRI	FRI	MON	WED	SAT
17	WED	SAT	SAT	TUE	THU	SUN ✿ Father's Da
18	THU	SUN	SUN	WED	FRI	MON
19	FRI	MON	MON	THU	SAT	TUE
20	SAT	TUE	TUE	FRI	SUN	WED
21	SUN	WED	WED	SAT ✿ The Queen's real birthday (Her official one moves around!)	MON	THU
22	MON	THU ✿ Girl Talk's 6th birthday!	THU	SUN	TUE	FRI
23	TUE	FRI	FRI	MON	WED	SAT
24	WED ✿ Yuan Tan (Chinese New Year)	SAT	SAT	TUE	THU	SUN
25	THU	SUN	SUN ✿ British Summer Time begins (Clocks go forward one hour) ✿ Mother's Day	WED	FRI	MON
26	FRI	MON	MON ✿ Al-Hijra (Muslim New Year's Day)	THU	SAT	TUE
27	SAT	TUE ✿ Shrove Tuesday (Pancake Day!)	TUE	FRI	SUN	WED
28	SUN	WED	WED	SAT	MON ✿ Spring Bank Holiday	THU
29	MON		THU	SUN	TUE	FRI
30	TUE		FRI	MON	WED	SAT
31	WED		SAT		THU	

PS Make sure you get your copy of Girl Talk every other Wednesday

PLANNER

Keep track of all your holidays and your mates' and family's birthdays!

JULY	AUGUST	SEPTEMBER	OCTOBER	NOVEMBER	DECEMBER	
SUN	WED	SAT	MON	THU	SAT	1
MON	THU	SUN	TUE	FRI	SUN	2
TUE	FRI	MON	WED	SAT	MON	3
WED	SAT	TUE	THU	SUN	TUE	4
THU	SUN	WED	FRI	MON ✿ Bonfire night	WED	5
FRI	MON	THU	SAT	TUE	THU	6
SAT	TUE	FRI	SUN	WED	FRI	7
SUN	WED	SAT	MON	THU	SAT	8
MON	THU	SUN	TUE	FRI	SUN	9
TUE	FRI	MON	WED	SAT	MON ✿ Hanukah begins	10
WED	SAT	TUE	THU	SUN	TUE	11
THU	SUN ✿ Janmashtami (the birthday of Lord Krishna)	WED	FRI	MON	WED	12
FRI	MON	THU	SAT	TUE	THU	13
SAT	TUE	FRI	SUN	WED ✿ Diwali begins (Hindu New Year and Hindu and Sikh Festival of Lights)	FRI	14
SUN	WED	SAT	MON	THU	SAT	15
MON	THU	SUN	TUE	FRI	SUN	16
TUE	FRI	MON	WED	SAT ✿ Ramadan begins (Muslim festival with fasting from dawn to dusk)	MON	17
WED	SAT	TUE ✿ Rosh Hashana (Jewish New Year)	THU	SUN	TUE	18
THU	SUN	WED	FRI	MON	WED	19
FRI	MON	THU	SAT	TUE	THU	20
SAT	TUE	FRI	SUN	WED	FRI	21
SUN	WED	SAT	MON	THU	SAT	22
MON	THU	SUN	TUE	FRI	SUN	23
TUE	FRI	MON	WED	SAT	MON	24
WED	SAT	TUE	THU	SUN	TUE ✿ Christmas Day (Christian festival celebrating the birth of Jesus)	25
THU	SUN	WED	FRI	MON	WED ✿ Boxing Day	26
FRI	MON ✿ Summer Bank Holiday	THU ✿ Yom Kippur (Day when Jews ask for God's forgiveness)	SAT	TUE	THU	27
SAT	TUE	FRI	SUN ✿ British Summer Time ends (Put those clocks back one hour!)	WED	FRI	28
SUN	WED	SAT	MON	THU	SAT	29
MON	THU	SUN	TUE	FRI	SUN	30
TUE	FRI		WED ✿ Halloween		MON	31

NOTES

NB Some major religious festivals are not fixed dates and should be confirmed nearer the time

Girl TALK

Animal rucksack

WHAT YOU'LL NEED
✿ **Grey fur fabric**
✿ **Glue** ✿ **Pen** ✿ **Ruler**
✿ **Scissors** ✿ **Black cord**
✿ **Safety pin** ✿ **Wobbly eyes and toy nose (from craft shops)** ✿ **Grey and red felt**

Make

You'll look really cool with thi brilliant backpack. Kirsten shows you how

Glue one end of each strip to a short edge of one of the rectangles, sticking the back of the strip fabric to the furry surface of the rectangle. Then let the strips lie flat over the surface of the rectangle.

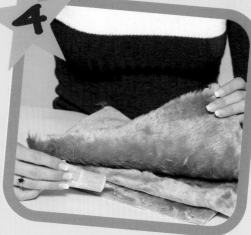

Fold the ends of the strips over the edge of the rectangle and glue them down. This time make sure the backs of the fabric are glued together.

Cut out two rectangles of fur fabric, 25cm by 30cm. Then cut out two narrower strips, 60cm by 6cm.

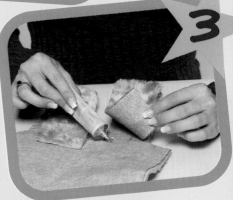

Glue the rectangles together along three edges, with the fur sides face to face. Leave the top edge unglued and open.

✿ Pictures: John Green ✿ Make it: Katie Sheffer ✿ Kirsten's top: Freemans

it!

5

Turn your bag out, so that the fur fabric is on the outside. Then snip holes at 4cm intervals round the opening of the bag. These should be 4cm down from the top edge.

6

Attach a safety pin to the end of a piece of cord. Then thread it in and out of the holes you have just made.

7

Glue on the eyes and nose and some felt shapes for a tongue and ears.

8

Now you just need to fill your bag with all your stuff and you're ready to go!

Are you the bestest of best friends or the poorest of pa...

20 **19**

If you sent [...] a card or birth[...] pressie on her[...] birthday, mo[...] forward 1 spa[...]

If you've phoned your best friend in the last three days, move forward 1 space.

22

38 **37**

23

If you've fallen out with your best friend in the last month, go back to Start.

FRIEN[...]

If you've cancelled an arrangement with your best friend in the last two weeks, move back 7 spaces.

40

Finish
Well done – you know just how important good friends are!

25

26

If you've lent anything to your pal in the last week, move forward 4 spaces.

28

Start

1 **2**

If you've seen your best friend in the last 24 hours, move forward 2 spaces.

4

Game: Claire Funge Ilustrations: Katy Taggart

Makeover magic!

Tired of your T-shirts? Fed up with your outfits? Well, here's three fab ways to customise your clothes and make your gear look groovy. Cool!

CHINA GIRL

Fabric strips and ribbons round the cuffs of your trousers are big news this year. But why pay a fortune for the look? You can make it really cheaply yourself – and even make a headscarf to match!

YOU WILL NEED

❀ Strong fabric (we used a lovely red Chinese design) ❀ Velvet ribbon ❀ Needle and cotton ❀ Tape measure ❀ Fabric glue

1 Measure the width of your trousers at the cuff then double it. Now cut two lengths of ribbon to the same measurement. Sew these in position round your cuff or stick them on with fabric glue.

2 If your trousers are not straight-legged, you will need to measure the width of your trousers again, above your new ribbon. If they are straight, you can now cut two strips of material to the same length as your ribbon. Make the strips about 10cm wide, to allow for a hem on each side.

3 Hem the strips along their length and then stitch or glue them in position above the ribbon. Make sure that where the ends meet is in the same position as the inside seam of the trousers. Turn the edges in and sew them in place.

4 Make a funky headscarf to complete your look by cutting a large triangle of material and hemming all the edges.

PERFECT PAINTS

There are lots of different fabric paints and crayons in the shops, and they are a great way to give clothes a completely new look. They're easy to use and, once fixed, you have a new permanent design. We recommend those that you fix by ironing.

YOU WILL NEED
✿ T-shirt ✿ Fabric paint (we used the kind that comes in tubes with a nozzle on the end, which makes applying your design a lot easier) ✿ Card ✿ Pencil ✿ An iron

1 Put your sheet of card inside your T-shirt. This gives you a firm flat surface to work on and stops paint seeping through to the back from the front of the T-shirt!

2 Draw your design very lightly in pencil on the front of your T-shirt. It won't matter if you don't follow the lines exactly, as the pencil will wash out.

3 Use your paints to fill in your design then leave it to dry.

4 Once it is dry, ask an adult to iron the design on the reverse side of the fabric, or according to the instructions on the tube. And there you have it – your own groovy design!

FLOWER POWER

Flowers are fab for a great girlie look. This is quick and easy to create, but so effective.

YOU WILL NEED
✿ Sleeveless T-shirt ✿ Ribbon rosebuds (available from fabric and crafts shops for about 16p each) ✿ Needle and cotton

1 Start by sewing a rosebud in the centre of the front of your T-shirt neckline.

2 Use this one as a guide and position other rosebuds right round the neckline – front and back. Space them evenly and sew them in place on the neckline and on the straps.

3 That's it – blooming marvellous!

✿ Words and styling: Claire Funge and Carol Gook ✿ Pictures: Mike Prior

continues over

Don't miss the *Girl Talk Best Friends* books

Creature comforts!

Want to know who the fluffy friends to the stars are? Well, look no further as we bring you a celebrity Meet My Pet special!

✿ Compiled by: Claire Funge ✿ Pictures: with thanks to *T.O.T.P. Magazine* (Geri) L&K Magazine (Jon) Rex Features (Shauna) Mike Prior (Sally)

Ana and Molly

We think Molly is two-and-a-half. We're not entirely sure because she was a rescue cat. I got her from the RSPCA when I was at university in Nottingham. She has a few funny habits. She dribbles when she is asleep and is scared of just about everything! She's becoming rather famous because I talk about her all the time on telly!

Our two dogs, Pan and Badger, are brothers and are collie crosses. We got them from a farm when they were six weeks old and they're now four! Pan is very greedy and tries to steal things out of the bin. But he's very laid back – almost to the point of being lazy! Badger is sensitive and scared of lots of things. He also loves to mother anything which is small, furry and makes squeaking noises!

Emma and Pan

Sally and Elsie

Elsie is seven years old now. I've had her since she was a tiny puppy. I love her very much. She's such a soppy thing. It was always a dream of mine to have a St Bernard. They do tend to dribble a lot, though! We have to have wooden floors throughout the house and no carpets!

Geri with Harry and Lucy

I sometimes dress them in cute little jumpers. Lucy has a bright pink jumper to make her look more feminine and Harry wears a funky blue tank top, which *Top of the Pops Magazine* gave him. He looks really rock 'n' roll!

Jon and Molly

Molly has lived with my family since she was nine weeks old. I used to do volunteer work at an animal distress centre and one day this litter of cute puppies came in. Molly was the runt and no one wanted her, so I just had to take her.

Shauna and Doc

Doc was given his name because of his white coat! We got him from our local rescue centre, the Ulster Society for Prevention of Cruelty to Animals, and he has become their mascot. He's very affectionate. His favourite TV programme is, of course, *Battersea Dogs Home!* He howls along to the music and goes mad when he hears my voice on TV. He's a bit of a celebrity now as he has appeared on *Live & Kicking* and CBBC.

Kate and Rio

This is Rio, my mare, at her stables. I've had her for three years and we've become very good friends. She's a very lively, fun horse even though she's no baby – she's 11 years old now! She can be a bit naughty, but I can't help spoiling her all the same. Best of all she likes carrots, apples and herballs, which are a horse treat.

TOP

Mrs Pointer was standing at the front of the class, reading out the spelling test results. "And the pupil with the most correct spellings is Lucy Williams," she announced. "Well, there's a surprise," someone muttered.

"Goody two-shoes," whispered another. Lucy tried to smile, but she felt like crying. It was always like this. Whenever she came top of the class someone made a nasty comment. She hated it. "Why can't they just leave me alone?" she whispered to her friend, Millie.

Class swot

"They think you're a swot, Luce," Millie said. "You're not, but they think you are." That night Lucy prepared her maths homework in her bedroom. As she worked through the sums, her dad popped his head round the door.

"Can I have a look at your homework?" he asked.

Lucy handed over her textbook. Her dad read through the pages. "Well, Lucy Locket, that's another top score," he beamed, handing the book back. "We'll see about that," Lucy muttered to herself. Carefully, she worked her way through the sums, making sure some of the answers were definitely incorrect. It didn't feel right but, after the day she had just had, it seemed like the only option. If she failed just a few tests, maybe her classmates would stop being so mean. The next day she handed the homework in. "Won't be any

DOG

A story by Justine Holman

problems with this, will there, Lucy?" her teacher said, smiling. "Swot," Claire mumbled. Lucy smiled to herself. If she had her way, no one was ever going to call her that again. Weeks passed and Lucy started to be a little more careless with her homework and her tests. At first no one took too much notice of her little failures. When she got just ten out of 20 for her maths homework her teacher said, "Having a bad day are we, Lucy?" And when she handed in her science project complete with dog footprints and the previous night's baked beans caked on the paper, all Mr Fox said was, "Oh dear, Lucy, it seems like having a little brother can be a bit hazardous sometimes."

The letter

But as the weeks went by teachers began to comment on her slipping grades. Where before she always had A's she was suddenly getting C's. Some teachers spoke to her after class to see if they could help. "Everything is fine," Lucy would tell them.
Eventually the headmistress sent a letter to her parents. She wanted to see them both in her office to "discuss Lucy's future". "Must be wanting to put you down for Cambridge!" her dad laughed when he saw the note. Lucy cringed. She didn't like flunking tests and she knew her parents would be furious, but life

at school had been almost bearable recently. There were less nasty comments and no scathing looks when the teacher

> **Some pupils only dreamt about coming top of the class. For Lucy it was a reality – a horrid reality**

announced results.
Even Mandy Robertson, the class bully, had stopped badgering her for homework answers. "I want someone with brains," she had laughed at Lucy. The following afternoon Lucy and her parents were sitting in the headmistress's office. "Mr and Mrs Williams, Lucy's grades have been slipping all term. She has fallen from first and second place to almost tenth in many of her lessons. Something is up, but we have no idea what."
"What's going on, Lucy?" her dad asked. "You normally do so well."
Lucy didn't say a word. "Are there problems at home?" asked the headmistress.
Her parents shook their heads. The headmistress looked at Lucy. "Why don't you tell us the problem?" she asked.
"What's up, Luce?" her mum whispered gently.
Lucy burst into tears. "I didn't want to do it," she sobbed, "but everyone makes fun of me for coming first all the time. I don't want to be top, I just want to be like everyone else."

"Now I see what has been going on," said the headmistress. "And I think I have the perfect solution."

Team work

The following day Lucy arrived at school early, as the headmistress had requested. Four other pupils were waiting outside her office. No one knew what they were there for.
The headmistress called them into her office. She quickly explained that she wanted Lucy and the others to help set up an after-school homework club, where pupils with difficulties could come for advice from fellow students and teachers. "It's one way we can use the talents of some of our best students to help those who are not so capable," she explained. "And it's a way of bringing you all together so that you can give each other support – as members of a team."
"But will it stop the name-calling?" Lucy muttered.
"Put it this way, Lucy." the head replied. "I hope people will stop making comments when they realise that you can all help them with different things. There's no point getting angry with someone who could help you solve a tough maths problem, is there?"
Lucy immediately saw the sense in the head's idea. Maybe she could learn to like being clever after all. And it would be nice not to have to work hard at getting things *wrong* any more. "Well, fingers crossed!" she said. ✿

Bored with your bedroom? Let **Girl Talk** give you a hand. We've got stacks of fab ideas to make your space look really cool

Room

What a load of old rubbish! Well, here's just the place to put it. Cover a bucket with fur fabric, trim with marabou and stick on another smart felt design. Just the place for those empty snack packets at sleepovers.

Sort out all your *Girl Talks* for starters! If you leave them under the bed, you'll only find they get all crumpled – or worse! Get hold of an old box file and give it a bit of a face-lift. Pick any theme you like.

A girl can never have enough storage! Your room will look really chic if everything is neat and tidied away. And boxes don't have to be boring when there are so many cool wrapping papers out there to give them any look you like.

Go potty! You can pick up terracotta pots really cheaply from almost anywhere selling garden stuff. Give them a little lick of paint, cover them with stickers, or cut out and stick on pictures, then finish them off with clear varnish. Now turn to pages 8 and 9 for fab ideas of what to put in them!

Pictures: John Green ✿ Make-its: Claire Funge, Jessica Dodd (door plate)

service!

SALLYS ROOM

Funky frames are a must. All those pictures of your pets and your bezzy pals have to go somewhere! Fluffy marabou is our fave, but you could use ribbon, lace, felt, tissue paper – just about anything!

It could say "Keep out" or just say your name. Make your own door nameplate for your own private room. Find a recipe for salt dough, then shape it, bake it, paint it and guess what? You've made it!

Mirror, mirror on the wall... Make a very professional bedroom mirror by sticking a small mirror (available very cheaply from most chemists) on to a card backing. Now you can go mad decorating it to match your own colour scheme.

Where do *you* keep your jim-jams? Under your pillow? On the floor! Well, why not make them a *Girl Talk* pyjama case? Cut an oblong of quilted material, fold it over side out and sew up the sides. Turn it the right way out and trim the top with lace. Put a funky felt design on the front for your own personalised pyjama case!

Wind chimes are so yesterday! Make your own stained-glass window instead. Cut a frame out of stiff cardboard. Stick coloured tissue papers over it and hang it in your window. Unfortunately we can't guarantee that the sun will shine!

Pillows aren't just for resting your weary head after a hard day at school. They can become part of your bedroom's look. So why not design your own? Fabric crayons are really easy to use. And if you're feeling really adventurous, you could do a duvet cover to match, but remember to check with Mum first! Sweet dreams.

47

ARE YOU A SUN SEEKER OR A WINTER-WORSHIPPER?

Does the weather set your mood? Are you only happy when it's sunny or do you have fun in the rain, too? Try our quiz to find out

1 **You've been saving up for two whole months and now you're ready to hit the shops. What do you buy?**
a) You have set your heart on a fab new vest top with matching headscarf and a brand new pair of shades to complete the outfit.
b) The latest fleeces and gilets are the first things you head for – they're just so snuggly.
c) You check out the sales racks and stock up on items that will last all year round.

2 **It's a really sunny Saturday, but your friends have all got plans of their own. What do you do?**
a) Grab your walkman, some sun screen and a beach towel, and spend a day lazing in the garden.
b) Close the curtains to block out the sun's glare then settle down to watch your favourite video.
c) Finish off your homework – after all, it's got to be done for Monday and your pals may be free tomorrow.

3 **Where would be your ideal place to live?**
a) In a beach house in Malibu, with the sand and the sea as your front garden.
b) In a wooden lodge in Austria, with snow on the ground so you

✿ Words: Kelly Wilks ✿ Illustrations: Katy Taggart

could ski all the way to school!

c) You love having your friends living near you and wouldn't wish to live anywhere else.

4 It's September and it has rained for the past three days. What do you think?

a) Summer seems impossibly far away and you'll not have any fun now until at least next spring.

b) It's great to listen to the sound of the rain on the windows, and even better to go outside and splash in the puddles.

c) The plants and trees in the garden will be really refreshed by the rain after the long hot summer.

5 When you think of summer what comes to mind?

a) Picnics, sunglasses, long evenings, and ice cream.

b) Hay fever, sunburn, hot classrooms and bees.

c) Endless summer holidays with absolutely no teachers, lessons or homework.

6 If you were an animal, what animal would you like to be?

a) A tropical fish. Just imagine spending your life swimming around in beautiful blue waters, beneath a bright sun.

b) A penguin. They always look like they're having such a cool time skidding around on ice and diving into the freezing water!

c) A cat. They get to spend all day playing out with their cat friends, but come home at night just in time for dinner and a warm place to sleep!

7 What would you do if you were stranded on a desert island?

a) Reach for the sun screen and pray you aren't rescued too quickly.

b) Search for a shaded area so you can keep cool and be protected from the powerful tropical sunshine.

c) Try to work out how on earth you're going to get home!

8 Your sister is getting married in November and wants you to be bridesmaid. What do you do?

a) Plead with her to have a summer wedding so that you can wear a short-sleeved dress and summer flowers in your hair.

b) Ask her to get married nearer Christmas and hope that it will snow – how gorgeous it would be to have

a white winter wedding!

c) Try on loads of dresses in the upcoming months to make sure yours will suit you perfectly on the day!

Mostly B's

Are you afraid you'll shrink in the sunlight? You seem to avoid it at all costs! You love nothing more than to be out and about, wrapped up warmly from head to toe, or curled up in front of the fire listening to the rain outside. It's great you don't let dark evenings and rain get you down, but by cutting out the sunshine you miss out. Building a snowman is fun, but a water fight in the garden with friends on a hot day can be hilarious.

Mostly A's

However do you cope from September to March? Your mood depends totally on the amount of sunshine in the day. If it's sunny, you're happy. But if it's not, there's just no pleasing you. Remember, it's only sunny for a fraction of the year so don't waste the rest of it longing for the sun to raise its blazing head. You can't control the seasons, so learn to enjoy all of them!

Mostly C's

When it comes to the weather, you've got the perfect and sensible attitude. You don't let anything as changeable as the elements get you down or stop you from having fun. You know some will be rainy days and some will be sunny, so you may as well make the most of all of them. The weather might be gloomy, but you will always be a little ray of sunshine!

Surf's

Time to log on and look into some of the coolest websites out on the net. Get your mouse at the ready...

B*Witched
http://www.b-witched.com
If you're a fan of B*Witched, you won't want to miss this B*Website! There's loads of info on their latest releases, lists of where you can see and read more about the girls, lots of fab facts and even video clips!

Send a card!
http://www.bluemountain.com
There's an electronic card for every occasion on this site. But who needs an occasion? There are cards here to send to friends and family just to say hello! And if you *are* looking for an occasion, then there's a diary of special days to help you find one!

Brownies
http://www.guides.org.uk
This is the official site for everything to do with Rainbows, Brownies and Guides. If you want to know what Brownies do, or about activities and camps, the Brownie promise or the uniform, it's all in here!

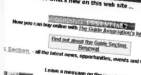

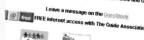

Compiled by Claire Funge

up!

Pokémon
http://www.pokemon.com
The official everything-to-do-with-Pokémon site! There's all the latest Pokémon news, answers to your Pokémon questions and some groovy wallpaper for your computer desktop!

Stories from the Web
http://hosted.ukoln.ac.uk/stories/
Get sneak previews of authors' and poets' latest works, talk to authors over the net and enter competitions. If you love stories, then this is the site for you. And if you live in Bristol, Birmingham or Leeds, you can actually join the Stories from the Web club at your central library (or the Compton Road Library in Leeds), where you can join in with activities and actually help to create your own web pages.

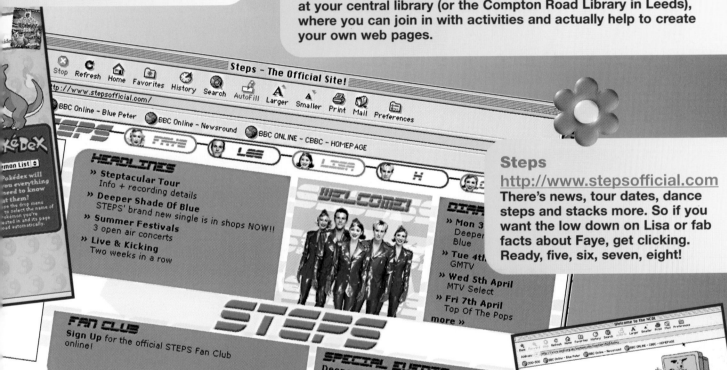

Steps
http://www.stepsofficial.com
There's news, tour dates, dance steps and stacks more. So if you want the low down on Lisa or fab facts about Faye, get clicking. Ready, five, six, seven, eight!

Kids' stuff
http://www.kidsdomain.co.uk
This site is just packed with loads of kids' stuff – games, recipes, clip art, stories, crafts and more. There are also sections for adults and teachers – but that's doesn't mean it's bad news for you. After all, there are pages for them reviewing the latest software for you – which might give them a few ideas for your birthday pressie!

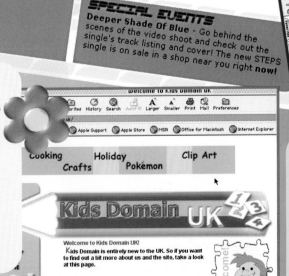

National Canine Defence League
http://www.ncdl.org.uk
Are you crazy about canines or daft about dogs? Then this is the place to be. Join the Smudge Supporters, find lots of top tips on caring for your pooch and even download a screensaver.

GARDENERS' WORLD

These are all things you may find in a garden. Can you dig them all out of the letter square?

```
W H H R F X B M M R F Z
M G Q V G D E T J F F Z
C V R W P E N L A O L K
F V Z E D B C I S O O H
V E I I E I H E E T W A
S P L F C N M L G B E M
H S O Q M O H U E A R M
E H W N N D Q O R L B O
D Y F G D I Z E U L E C
S W I N G A Z M N S D K
P E H O S E P I P E E Q
W A S H I N G L I N E M
```

HOSE PIPE SWING FOOTBALL SHED
GREENHOUSE FLOWER BED BENCH
HAMMOCK POND WASHING LINE
GNOMES SLIDE

VEG OUT!

Cross out all the letters that appear more than once. The remaining letters should spell out a comfy part of the house

_ _ _ _ _ _ _ _

```
B L Q I F P
J H M O K A
C U R H B M
F S T N S D
K A T J G R
D Q E C P I
```

Sleepy head

Complete these words using the clues and the missing letters will spell out a special spot for two

SY   WI
_ _ _ _ _ _ _ _
GRA_

TIR_   _NORE

1. When you have lots and lots to do
2. To close just one eye
3. To snatch something quickly
4. How you feel at the end of a long day
5. A noise people make in their sleep

_ _ _ _ _ _ _ _ _ _

HOME FRONT

Can you turn a hall into a seat in four steps by changing just one letter at a time?

H A L L

_ _ _ _

_ _ _ _

_ _ _ _

S E A T

Sweet dreams

Fit the names of these objects into the correct spaces to reveal the name of a room in the shaded squares

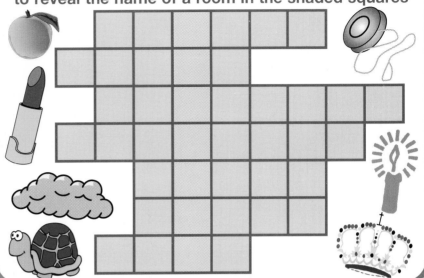

RELAXING REMEDIES

Melanie, Camilla and Marie all relax in different ways at home. Follow the lines to find out what each does

Melanie

Camilla

Marie

Clothes horse

Take the first letter from the name of each object and rearrange them all to name a piece of bedroom furniture

_ _ _ _ _ _ _ _

_ _ _ _ _   _ _ _ _   _ _ _ _ _ _

53

My name's Polly and I'm mad about history. I know, it sounds boring doesn't it? But it's not. It's great finding out all about people who lived a long time ago. The trouble is all my friends think history is as dull as ditchwater. All of them, that is, except Saffron. She lives a long way away, but we write to each other every week and she knows all my secrets. Saffron and I got to know each other a long time before we met. I was fed up because I didn't have anyone to talk to about my hobby. "Why don't you get a pen pal?" suggested Mum. "Write to *Girl Talk.* You might find someone with the same interests as you."

Perfect friend

So I filled out the form. I put my hobbies as history and animals. Then I sent it off and waited to see if it would be printed. It was and I got quite a few replies, but Saffron's was the best. "Dear Polly," she wrote, "you sound just like me. I love history, too. And I love animals. I've got a dog called Scruff and there are seals on the island where I live. I hope we can be friends. Love, Saffron xxx."

She sounded perfect and I was just about to write back when I noticed her address. Lochkin Castle, Isle of Mur, Scotland. This girl lived in a castle! I just live in a flat with my mum. So I guessed we didn't have

> I pictured Saffron sitting on her throne in a long velvet dress covered in jewels

much in common after all. I thought she must be mega rich to live in a castle, maybe even a princess. I imagined a beautiful castle with gleaming turrets. And I pictured Saffron sitting on her throne in a long velvet dress covered in jewels. I looked round at the peeling posters on my bedroom wall. Then I looked down sadly at my scruffy old jeans and trainers. "I don't think Saffron would want to be my friend," I said to Mum that evening. "She wouldn't have written if she didn't want a pen pal," said Mum. I still wasn't sure, but I wrote back anyway. And Mum was right. Saffron did write back.

The visit

We wrote to each other every week after that, but Saffron never mentioned the castle. We mostly talked about our history projects. Saffron loved the Victorians. Having a pen friend

was great fun. But then she invited me to stay. "I can't go, Mum," I said. "Why not?" said Mum. "Because then Saffron will know I'm just ordinary. I'm not really rich like her."

Mum persuaded me to go, but I was still worried. Finally the holidays arrived. It was a long drive but Mum had packed loads of sandwiches and crisps and we had lots of stops on the way. "Enjoy your sandwiches," Mum joked. "You won't be eating food this ordinary when you get to the castle!" We had to take a ferry to get to Saffron's island. There was only one ferry a day and we arrived just as it was about to leave.

Haunted castle

The island looked beautiful from the ferry. As the waves lashed the side of the boat I felt really excited about meeting my friend. But then I spotted the castle and my heart sank. It was a ruin. There were no sparkling turrets. In fact, it was hardly more than a pile of old bricks. And it looked really spooky. I shivered. Where was I going to sleep? I couldn't stay there. It was bound to be haunted. "Mum, I'm

Princess

A story by Alison Viña

great to meet you finally."

"You, too," I answered nervously.

It wasn't far to the castle and as we got nearer my heart started to race. We were a short walk away when Saffron stopped.

"We're here," she smiled as she walked up the path to a pretty cottage.

Best holiday

"You live here?" I asked. "But, I thought you lived in the castle."

Saffron laughed. "I wouldn't fancy living inside that, would you?" We live here in the grounds. My dad manages the estate. It's his job to make sure that everything is all right when the tourists visit."

"So you're not a princess?" I asked.

"Of course not," Saffron giggled. "Come on in. Tea's ready."

I had the best holiday of my life. Saffron's dad even gave us a private tour of the castle, which was amazing. And we saw loads of seals. Next holiday Saffron's promised to visit me in my flat. And do you know what? I can't wait to show her round. ✿

scared," I gulped as I grasped her hand.

Saffron met us from the ferry and she didn't look like a princess at all. She wasn't wearing a velvet dress or any jewels. In fact, she was wearing jeans and trainers just like me. "Hi, Polly," she smiled. "It's

RUNAWAY HAMSTER
Part 4

Tinkerbell, the school hamster, is still missing

What are you two doing?

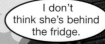
I don't think she's behind the fridge.

This packet of biscuits has really been chewed.

They're Tinkerbell's favourite.

We think Tinkerbell is still in the house, Mum!

Can hamsters open doors?

I've caught something in my mousetrap.

Have you hurt it?

No. There's definitely something in there. Listen!

Squeak. Squeak.

Grab her or she'll escape again.

Do you like her now?

My trap works! I told you that it wouldn't hurt her.

I think so. She's pretty nice really.

Next morning

What's in the box?

Tinkerbell! She was at home all the time!

Now she can be friends Thumbelina.

And we have two hamsters to take home!

Poor Tink. She could be stuck somewhere.

She may not be in the kitchen anymore. She could be anywhere.

Come quickly!

Why? What is it?

Tinkerbell!

Squeak. Squeak.

Hey, she's all soft and her whiskers are tickly.

They look just the same.

We know.

They're twins – just like us!

THE END

You can read more of the twins' adventures every fortnight in

Girl TALK